HOPSCOTCH HISTORIES

Florence
and the
Drummer Boy

by Penny Dolan

Illustrated by Lesley Bisseker

W
FRANKLIN WATTS
LONDON•SYDNEY

About this book

Some of the characters in this book are made up but the story is based on real events in history. Florence Nightingale (1820–1910) trained to be a nurse in 1851. A few years later, the Crimean War (1853–1856) started. Florence took 20 nurses and went to help the injured British soldiers in a hospital in Scutari (Turkey). She was called the 'Lady with the Lamp' as she checked on the soldiers at night. After the war, she returned to London as a celebrity. In 1860, she set up the Nightingale Training School for nurses in St Thomas' hospital. She spent the rest of her life campaigning to make hospitals cleaner.

First published in 2009 by
Franklin Watts
338 Euston Road
London
NW1 3BH

Franklin Watts Australia
Level 17/207 Kent Street
Sydney
NSW 2000

Text © Penny Dolan 2009
Illustrations © Lesley Bisseker 2009

The right of Penny Dolan to be identified as the author
and Lesley Bissker as illustrator of this Work has been asserted
in accordance with the Copyright, Designs and Patents Act, 1988.

A CIP catalogue record for this book is available
from the British Library.

ISBN 978 0 7496 8574 4 (hbk)
ISBN 978 0 7496 8580 5 (pbk)

Series Editor: Melanie Palmer
Series Advisor: Dr Barrie Wade
Series Designer: Peter Scoulding

Printed in China

Franklin Watts is a division of
Hachette Children's Books,
an Hachette UK company
www.hachette.co.uk

Billy was a drummer boy in the
British army. His drum sounded
out orders to the soldiers in battle.

Then one day – BANG!

Billy fell to the ground.

"Quick, get him to hospital!"
someone cried.

4

When Billy woke up, his arm
and leg hurt. He looked scared.
"You're in Florence Nightingale's
hospital now," a young soldier said.

Billy looked around. The hospital was clean and tidy. There were lots of injured soldiers in rows of beds.

Just then a tortoise walked past!
"That's Jimmy. He's our ward pet,"
said one injured soldier.

"Miss Nightingale likes keeping animals," said a nurse. "They help to make the soldiers happy."

Billy liked animals, too. He wanted to meet Miss Nightingale and thank her for his treatment.

One day, as Billy began to get better, he asked the nurse, "Please can I meet Miss Nightingale?"

"She only comes round at night,"
the nurse replied. "She's too busy in
the daytime running the hospital."

Billy rested and watched Jimmy carry things to the soldiers. He saw how they sent notes to each other.

The soldiers read books and sang songs. They mended clothes and played games.

One night, it was too hot to sleep.
Billy saw a lady with a lamp
standing at his bedside.

"Are you Miss Nightingale?" he asked.

"Yes," Florence replied. "I've brought
you some water."

Billy found Florence very kind. She asked him about his arm and his leg. "They still hurt," he told her, "but not as much."

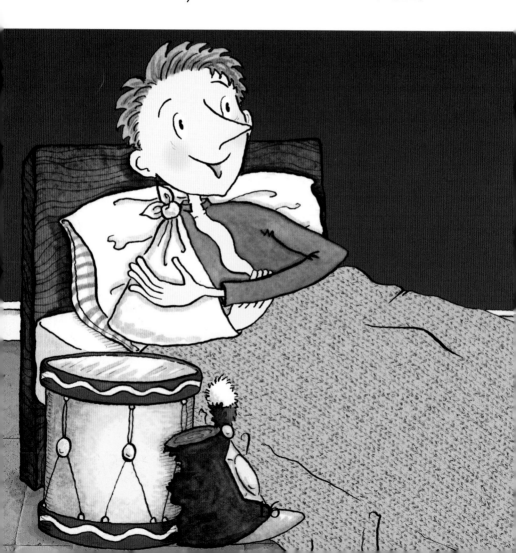

"You're a brave boy, Billy," Florence said. "Keep trying to rest." Then she went to see the next patient.

Each day, Billy felt better. Soon he could get up, but his arm still hurt. Florence came back to see him.

"You won't be able to be a drummer boy anymore, Billy. But perhaps you can help me."

When he felt well enough, Billy helped the nurses in the hospital. He also visited the other patients.

Florence worked so hard that she got sick with a fever. Billy took Jimmy to visit Florence. The soldiers sent her get well letters, too.

When Florence recovered, she decided it was time to go back to England. "I want to open a hospital there."

"Will you come and help me?"
she asked Billy.

"Yes please!" Billy cried, happily.

As soon as they arrived in London,
Florence set to work. She met lots
of important people. "We need to
have more good nurses," she said.

Florence became famous. Many
people wrote asking for her help.
"So many letters! I can't answer
them all myself," she told Billy.

Billy learnt a lot from Florence.
When he got older, he became
a doctor's assistant.

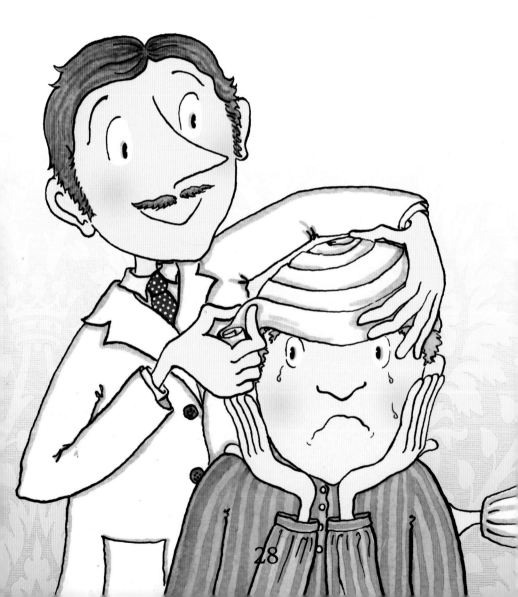

Florence kept busy for the rest of her life, but sometimes she came back to see Billy.

Puzzle 1

Put these pictures in the correct order.

Which event do you think is most important?

Now try writing the story in your own words!

Word Bank

Cards
Clean
Letters
Nurse
Reading
Sewing

What do these pictures tell you about how hospitals changed during Florence's lifetime?

How are things different today?

You can use the word bank to help you.

Answers

Puzzle 1

The correct order is: 1d, 2c, 3e, 4a, 5f, 6b.

Puzzle 2

Hospitals changed a lot in Florence Nightingale's lifetime.
Think about diseases, nurses, war and medicines.

For more information, try this book:

Florence Nightingale, (History Makers), Sarah Ridley,
Franklin Watts, 2009.